1

Parents Orators Writers Artists Readers

P.o.w.a.r

A Family Learning Project

Other books from the Powar series include the Intermediate Reader, 'Weeding Cane' and two anthologies, 'The Power From Within' and 'Our Say'. Please check the back of this book for details of the Powar Poster Collection.

2

Learn to Listen, Then You Won't Feel

Paulette Martin

NATIONAL
LOTTERY
CHARITIES
BOARD

Powar Project Co-ordinator, Leroy Williamson
Crèche Co-ordinator, Elizabeth Aryee
Text copyright © Paulette Martin. 2001
Editor, Leroy Williamson
Illustrations, Ian Bobb
Design, Ian Bobb and Leroy Williamson

Published & distributed by Gatehouse Books Ltd.
Hulme Adult Education Centre, Stretford Road, Manchester M15 5FQ.
Printed by RAP Ltd, Clock Street, Hollinwood, Oldham, Lancs. OL9 7LY.
ISBN 0 906253 96 9
British Library cataloguing in publication data:
A catalogue record for this book is available from the British Library

'Learn to Listen, Then You Won't Feel' was developed from writing originally produced
by Paulette Martin with editor, Leroy Williamson. The writing was drawn from
workshops during the Powar family learning project at Claremont Infant School,
Moss Side, Manchester.

One Gatehouse reading circle recommended this story for publication. Many thanks
for their work to Steph Prior, Sonia Hammond, Susan Armstrong, Wendy Gibbons,
Monica Ebanks and Joseph Campbell.

Thanks also to the English and Basic Skills groups run by Manchester Adult Education
Services at Ducie Adult Education Centre and Greenheys Adult Education Centre with
whom we piloted a first draft of this book.

Special thanks also to Judy Craven, Sonia Hammond, Ruth Nunes, Harvey Nisbett and
Pat Lee who were instrumental to the success of the project.

Gatehouse acknowledges grant aid towards the production of this book from The
National Lottery and Manchester City Council.

Gatehouse is a member of The Federation of Worker Writers & Community Publishers.

Gatehouse provides an opportunity for writers to express their thoughts and feelings
on aspects of their lives. The views expressed are not necessarily those of Gatehouse.

Introduction

Hello, my name is Paulette Martin.
I am the writer of the story.

'Learn to Listen, Then You Won't Feel' is based
on a true story and was created from a workshop idea
looking at how to write a story for children and adults.

I wrote it to tell my children that once I was their age
and sometimes I was naughty and so I dedicate it to
them, Hanna, Kerith and Nathaneal.
I hope you enjoy it too.

Paulette Martin

Kim had been told
not to go into the biscuit tin.
She had already eaten her dinner
and it was good!
Fried dumplings, golden brown,
spicy baked beans cooked with onions,
her favourite,
and finally scrambled eggs.

She had eaten every bit
and had drunk
the sweet yet creamy drink,
with the nutmeg and cinnamon spices
which her mum had made
to go with the meal.
Now her tummy was full, very full.

That however,
did not stop her
from spying
the multi-coloured biscuit tin.
It was usually placed
in the kitchen next to the bread bin
and was easy to reach.
Her favourites
were the shortbread biscuits
and if there was none,
the digestives were always
good to have with jam, especially strawberry!

But Mum
did not want her to have any
in case she became sick.
She knew her daughter liked biscuits.
And so the biscuit tin
was moved away from the breadbin
and placed on top
of the highest kitchen cupboard.

They could have one each
and then they would not be hungry,
but she remembered
what her mum had said,
"No more biscuits, not one!"
"It's only a few biscuits
and Mum won't really mind
if I give some to the others,
after all, they are hungry."

Her mind made up, she said,
"Okay, we can get some biscuits
and that will make you feel alright
but how are we going to get them?"

They looked in the kitchen;
they looked in the bathroom.
Finally, they found what they needed
in the living room,
Mum's best dining room chairs.

Six black wooden chairs
with a yellow cushion for a seat.
Quickly and quietly
the children moved one chair each
from around the table and into the
kitchen.

They placed first one chair
in front of the cupboard
where the biscuit tin was
but when the little girl
stood on the chair in her socks
she only reached the handle of the cupboard.

Another chair was placed
on top of the first.
The legs of the chair
made a deep mark in the cushion.
Very carefully, Kim climbed the two chairs
whilst her brother and sister
stood in the kitchen doorway
listening and watching out
for Mum and Dad.
Kim stood on the second chair.
It was very high
and she became a little scared
but she wasn't too far
from the biscuit tin now,
only one more chair.

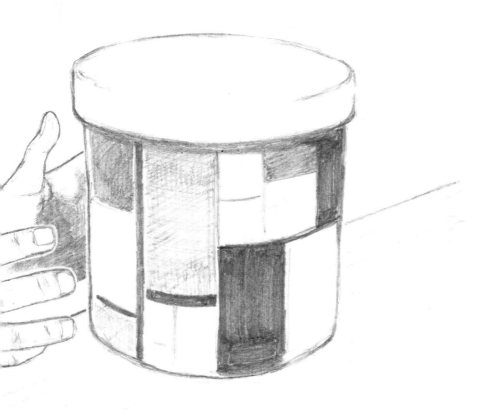

"That was so easy,"
she said to her brother and sister
who seemed so small to her
looking from the ceiling of the kitchen.
Without thinking
she began to open the biscuit tin.

It was a little hard
so she pulled at the lid
forgetting to hold on to the cupboard.
"Oh no," the little girl cried.

Kim felt the chair wobble
and then tip backwards
away from the cupboard
and with biscuit tin in hand,
she fell from the highest chair,
hitting the floor
with a thud!

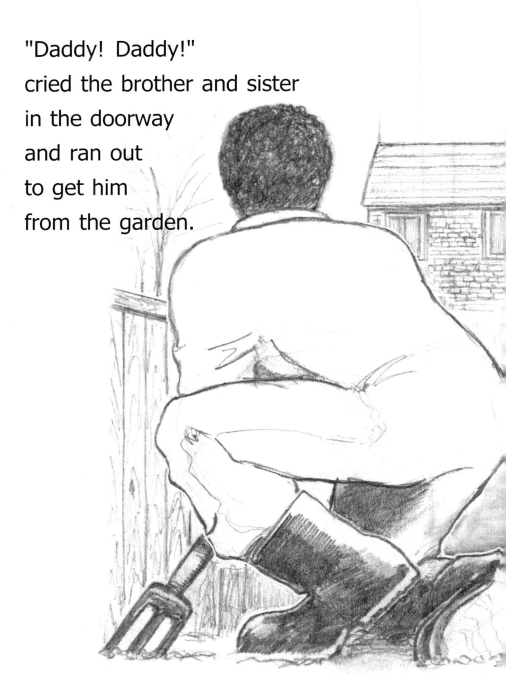

"Daddy! Daddy!"
cried the brother and sister
in the doorway
and ran out
to get him
from the garden.

28

Dad came into the kitchen
and found Kim lying on the floor crying,
a biscuit clutched in her hand,
the chairs lying either side of her.

"I only wanted to get us some biscuits," she cried.

Dad then rushed to the phone.

Nathan and Hannah stood at the door frightened and shaking.

Their sister had hurt herself in the fall and was now bleeding from her ear.

The key slowly turned in the front door.
"I'm home," said Mum
walking into the kitchen
laden with shopping.
"Oh no," she said,
as she dropped the bags
and rushed to the little girl's side.

"What happened?"
Dad quickly came into the kitchen.
"I've just phoned for an ambulance,
they'll be here shortly."
"I only wanted to get us some biscuits,
we were hungry," Kim said.
"But don't you remember what I said?"
replied Mum, a little upset herself.

"If you had listened to what I said
you wouldn't be in pain now."
Gently she held her hand.
"We'll wait for the ambulance."
The ambulance arrived
and quickly the family
were taken to the hospital.
Once inside,
Kim was taken by a nurse
into a room
where they used a special camera
to photograph what happened to her
body.

Mum and Dad explained
that the photograph was an x-ray
and that it would let the doctor know
if a bone or muscle inside her body
had been broken or hurt.
"No damage done,"
said the doctor to Mum and Dad,
"but she has to rest her left knee
as she has hurt it badly in the fall."
Mum and Dad
thanked the doctors and nurses
and the family left the hospital
and then made their way home
with Kim's knee bandaged.

On the way, Kim said to her Mum,
"I'm sorry Mum,
I should have listened to you
and done as you told me."
Mum looked at her children
and said kindly,
"I would never tell you something
for no reason.
I will always care for you,
whether you are good or bad but....

**if you don't listen to what I say,
you will feel!"**

Set of 8 original full colour posters.
2 pack sizes available - A2 or A3

For an order form please call Gatehouse Books on 0161 226 7152.

The posters reflect positive images of mothers and their children. Writing produced by the parent complements each poster. The collection supports the belief that parents are the first and most important teachers of a child.

Positive images of parents and children of African descent are rare. These posters will document, inspire and promote the value of families learning together and from each other.

The term 'parent' in the above instance applies equally to a child's carer or guardian.

36

Gatehouse Books

Gatehouse is a unique publisher

Our writers are adults who are developing their basic reading and writing skills. Their ideas and experiences make fascinating material for any reader, but are particularly relevant for adults working on their reading and writing skills. The writing strikes a chord – a shared experience of struggling against many odds.

The format of our books is clear and uncluttered. The language is familiar and the text is often line-broken, so that each line ends at a natural pause.

Gatehouse books are both popular and respected within Adult Basic Education throughout the English speaking world. They are also a valuable resource within secondary schools, Social Services and within the Prison Education Service and Probation Services.

Booklist available

Gatehouse Books
Hulme Adult Education Centre
Stretford Road
Manchester
M15 5FQ.
Tel and Fax: 0161 226 7152
E-mail: office@gatehousebooks.org.uk
Website: www.gatehousebooks.org.uk

The Gatehouse Publishing Charity Ltd is a registered charity, no 1011042
Gatehouse Books Ltd is a company limited by guarantee reg. no. 2619614